Black Girls Make Magic

Author
Ms. Shaneice White

Illustrator
Sameer Kassar

Dedication:

This book is dedicated to my beautiful Goddaughter and all of the young girls around the world.

My name is Destiny!

And I am a black girl.

And if you've ever heard anything bad about black girls...

Then you've heard wrong! I mean terribly wrong!

So please, check your source...

Because it should say "Black Girls Make Magic, everyday in every way!"

Whenever I am at school, there's magic to be made.

Sometimes, girls who don't look like me whisper and laugh about my hair.

But, I never respond, I just close my eyes and visualize what momma would say.

I know Momma would say something like, "Destiny, you should never care what they think of your hair because they are just trying to figure out its magic."
So, my hair does only what man can do on the moon and that's defy Gravity!

My skin is magical. It is beautiful and dark, and it protects me from the sun. My skin is special because it has all the colors of the rainbow in it.

Whenever other kids make fun, I always remember the beautiful queens of Africa and my momma's words.

"Whenever they judge your skin, look into the mirror and say, 'I love you'," my momma always tells me.

And so, I do!

"Destiny, I love you so much!" I even give myself a big hug!

But not only do black girls make magic
through our looks.
Nor is school the only place we make magic.

We make magic out in public...
We make magic in our church...
We make magic in our homes...

Our presence everywhere is simply magical.

We also make magic by jumping the hurdles of life.

Whenever I feel low or I lack confidence
in myself…

I remember to always keep my head held
high and to adjust my crown.

"This too shall pass," I say to myself
because my mom taught me that nothing
lasts forever.

Black girls make magic when we believe in and respect ourselves.

"Destiny, you can do anything you put your mind to," I tell myself. And I have my mom to thank for that because she tells me that all the time.

Black girls make magic when we know our worth. I know my worth. Do you?
Black girls even make magic when it is time to go to bed at night.

I fall asleep and dream of all the wonderful things I am...
And all the wonderful things I will become!
So, black girls near and far, speak highly of yourselves.

Say it with me:

I am beautiful!

I am smart!

I am brave!

I am loving!

I am capable!

And most of all...

I am magical!

I am black and I make magic!

The End

About the author:

Ms. Shaneice White was born and raised in Madison, WI. After graduating from high school she went on to attend San Diego State University, where she earned her BS in Child and Family Development with additional studies in Cultural Proficiency and Counseling/ Social Change. Ms. White is currently an elementary school teacher in the heart of Metro Atlanta. She is also pursuing her M.Ed in Elementary Education at Grand Canyon University.

Ms.White has a profound passion for young children, traveling, and education. She strongly believes that representation within the books that children read matter. Follow Ms.White's journey as she continues to use her gift of resilience, determination, and passion to empower young minds; the future of our nation!

Made in the USA
Coppell, TX
10 February 2021